SAMU
AND TH
WAKE-
CALL

1 Samuel 1–3 for Children

Written by Jane L. Fryar
Illustrated by Elizabeth Swisher

ARCH® Books
Copyright © 1994 Concordia Publishing House
3558 S. Jefferson Avenue, St. Louis, MO 63118-3968
Manufactured in the United States of America

In Israel long, long ago
The people of the land were sad.
They lived in sin, they lied and stole,
They fought and made each other mad.

They would not listen to the Lord,
Would not respect His Word or name.
To this unholy, awful mess
The prophet known as Samuel came.

His father's name? Elkanah. And
One thing about him you should know:
He had two wives—a big mistake.
Back then, not all folks thought it so.

Peninnah's children filled the house.
They brought Elkanah lots of joy.
But Hannah hadn't had a child.
She wanted one—a girl or boy.

Elkanah tried to comfort her;
Peninnah ridiculed and teased.
Their home was not a happy place.
Elkanah often was displeased.

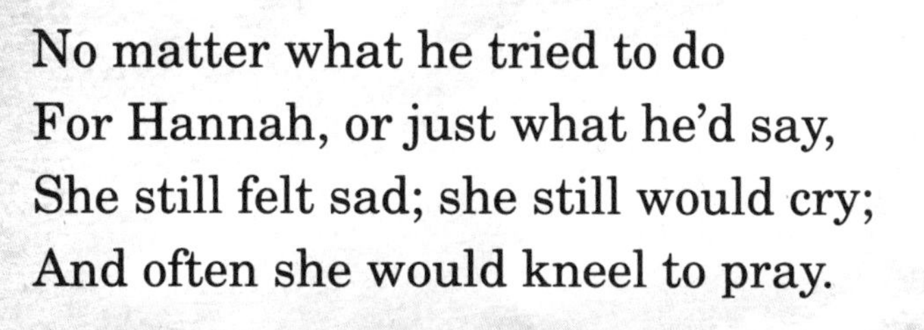

No matter what he tried to do
For Hannah, or just what he'd say,
She still felt sad; she still would cry;
And often she would kneel to pray.

Once every year Elkanah took
His family up to Shiloh where
They worshiped, praised, and thanked the Lord.
A priest named Eli served God there.

One year the family made a feast
At Shiloh on a holy day;
And when the family meal was done
Sad Hannah slowly crept away.

She opened up her heart to God.
"Dear Lord," she said, "You are the one
Who always gives good things to us.
Please, God, give to me a son.

"Remember me, and show Your love
And then, dear Lord, here's what I'll do—
When he is old enough to serve,
I'll give him back, O Lord, to You."

Now Eli watched while Hannah prayed.
He saw her cry a flood of tears.
He thought, “She’s drunk, and that is why
Her heart is filled with many fears.”

He scolded her, but she said, “No!
I am not drunk as you suppose;
I’m filled with sadness, but the Lord
Will help me.” With that, Hannah rose.

Her grief touched Eli's heart. He said,
"Go now, my child, God heard your prayer.
May He give you just what you've asked.
May He remove your every care."

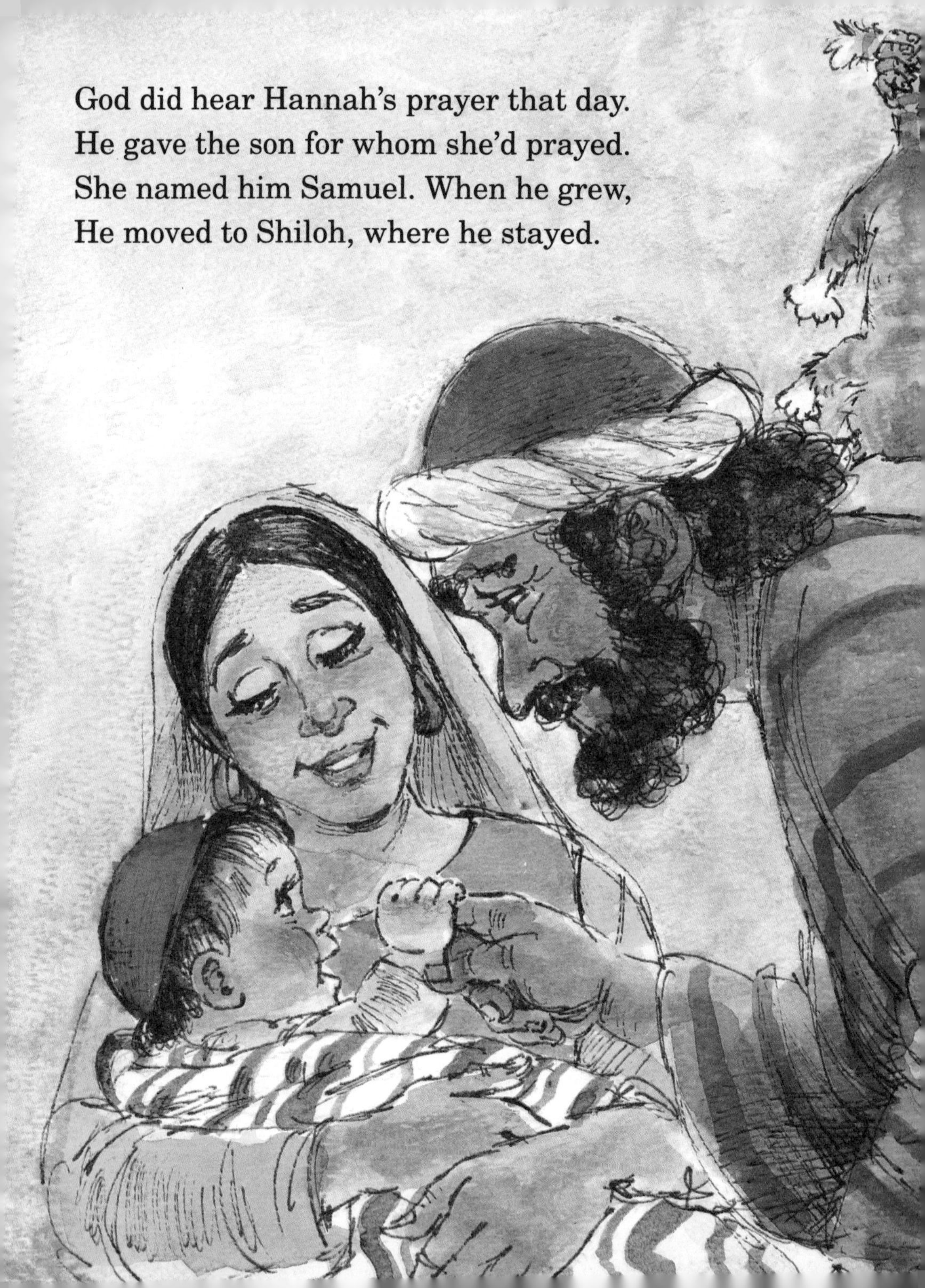

God did hear Hannah's prayer that day.
He gave the son for whom she'd prayed.
She named him Samuel. When he grew,
He moved to Shiloh, where he stayed.

Now Eli had two grown-up sons
Who lived with him at Shiloh too.
But they were wicked men who stole
From God. And even Eli knew.

Still, he did nothing. So the Lord
Sent prophets warning, “Stop them. Now!”
But Eli shrugged. He did not know
Quite what to do, or when or how.

One night as Samuel lay in bed
He heard his name. Did Eli call?
He got up and he went to see,
But Eli had not called at all.

It happened two more times that night.
Poor Samuel couldn't sleep. Or try!
The third time Eli said, "The Lord
Is calling you. You must reply:

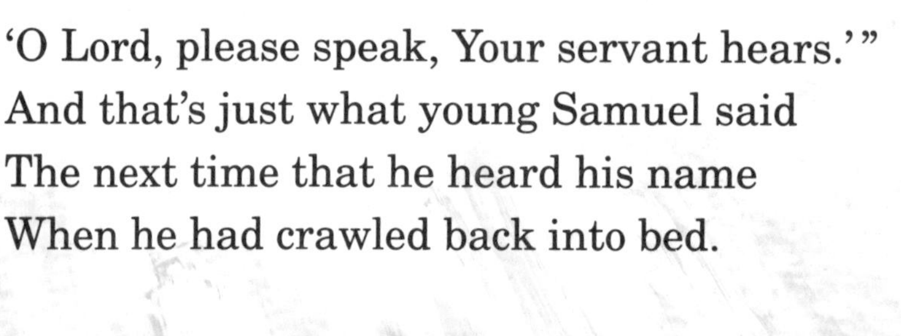

'O Lord, please speak, Your servant hears.'"
And that's just what young Samuel said
The next time that he heard his name
When he had crawled back into bed.

The Lord told him that Eli's sons
Deserved His anger—it was true!
God said that He would punish them
For all they'd done and yet would do.

God did exactly what He'd said,
And that same night Samuel became
A prophet—spokesman—for the Lord.
To him God's people often came.

He taught them of God's will, God's love,
And of the Savior God would send.
He was, you'd say, God's gift to them.
He was, by God's great grace, their friend.

Dear Parents:

Children are a gift from God; they are His reward (Psalm 127:3). How wonderful it is when parents and grandparents, aunts, uncles, and teachers recognize children as God's gifts. How much more wonderful still when they remind the children in their care of this fact.

From an early age, Samuel must have heard the story of his birth. From little on, Samuel must have heard Hannah and Elkanah, and perhaps even Eli, too, remind him of what a unique and precious gift from God he was.

Are we unique? Are we precious? Look at the cross. Consider the price paid there to rescue us—each one of us—from sin and death. What are we worth? Look at what God paid for us! The life of His only Son.

Samuel saw that cross dimly. He saw it through the mists of the centuries that were yet to come. We see it clearly. We see it as the proof, the once-for-all-time proof of the Father's love for us.

Share that love with the children close to you. Share it often. It's the most important thing in life.

The Editor